Contents

Introduction

Attention deficit hyperactivity disorder (ADHD) is a mental health disorder that can cause above-normal levels of hyperactive and impulsive behaviors. People with ADHD may also have trouble focusing their attention on a single task or sitting still for long periods of time.

Both adults and children can have ADHD. It's a diagnosis the American Psychiatric Association (APA) recognizes.

Learn about types of ADHD and symptoms in both children and adults.

ADHD symptoms

A wide range of behaviors are associated with ADHD. Some of the more common ones include:

- having trouble focusing or concentrating on tasks
- being forgetful about completing tasks
- being easily distracted
- having difficulty sitting still
- interrupting people while they're talking

If you or your child has ADHD, you may have some or all of these symptoms. The symptoms you have depend on the type of ADHD you have. Explore a list of ADHD symptoms common in children.

Types of ADHD

To make ADHD diagnoses more consistent, the APA has grouped the condition into three categories, or types. These types are predominantly inattentive, predominantly hyperactivity-impulsive, and a combination of both.

Predominantly inattentive

As the name suggests, people with this type of ADHD have extreme difficulty focusing, finishing tasks, and following instructions. Experts also think that many children with the inattentive type of ADHD may not receive a proper diagnosis because they don't tend to disrupt the classroom. This type is most common among girls with ADHD.

Predominantly hyperactive-impulsive type

People with this type of ADHD show primarily hyperactive and impulsive behavior. This can include fidgeting, interrupting people while they're talking, and not being able to wait their turn.

Although inattention is less of a concern with this type of ADHD, people with predominantly hyperactive-impulsive ADHD may still find it difficult to focus on tasks.

Combined hyperactive-impulsive and inattentive type

This is the most common type of ADHD. People with this combined type of ADHD display both inattentive and hyperactive symptoms. These include an inability to pay attention, a tendency toward impulsiveness, and above-normal levels of activity and energy.

The type of ADHD you or your child has will determine how it's treated. The type you have can change over time, so your treatment may change, too. Learn more about the three types of ADHD.

ADD vs. ADHD

You may have heard the terms "ADD" and "ADHD" and wondered what the difference is between them. ADD, or attention deficit disorder, is an outdated term. It was previously used to describe people who have problems paying attention but aren't hyperactive. The type of

ADHD called predominantly inattentive is now used in place of ADD.

ADHD is the current overarching name of the condition. The term ADHD became official in May 2013, when the APA released the Diagnostic and Statistical Manual of Mental Disorders, Fifth Edition (DSM-5).

Adult ADHD

More than 60 percentTrusted Source of children with ADHD still exhibit symptoms as adults. But for many people, ADHD symptoms decrease or become less frequent as they get older.

That said, treatment is important. Untreated ADHD in adults can have a negative impact on many aspects of life. Symptoms such as trouble managing time, forgetfulness, and impatience can cause problems at work, home, and in all types of relationships. Find out more about the signs and symptoms of ADHD in adults and how they can impact your life.

ADHD in children

One in 10 children between ages 5 to 17 years receives an ADHD diagnosis, making this one of the most common childhood neurodevelopmental disorders in the United States. For children, ADHD is generally associated with problems at school. Children with ADHD often have trouble succeeding in a controlled classroom setting.

Boys are more than twice as likely as girls to receive an ADHD diagnosis. This may be because boys tend to exhibit hallmark symptoms of hyperactivity. Although some girls with ADHD may have the classic symptoms of hyperactivity, many don't. In many cases, girls with ADHD may:

- daydream frequently
- be hyper-talkative rather than hyperactive

Many symptoms of ADHD can be typical childhood behaviors, so it can be hard to know what's ADHD-related and what's not. Learn more about how to recognize ADHD in toddlers.

What causes ADHD

Despite how common ADHD is, doctors and researchers still aren't sure what causes the condition. It's believed to have neurological origins. Genetics may also play a role.

Research suggests that a reduction in dopamine is a factor in ADHD. Dopamine is a chemical in the brain that helps move signals from one nerve to another. It plays a role in triggering emotional responses and movements.

Other research suggests a structural difference in the brain. Findings indicate that people with ADHD have less gray matter volume. Gray matter includes the brain areas that help with:

- speech
- self-control

- decision-making
- muscle control

Researchers are still studying potential causes of ADHD, such as smoking during pregnancy. Find out more about the potential causes and risk factors of ADHD.

ADHD testing and diagnosis

There's no single test that can tell if you or your child has ADHD. A recent study highlighted the benefits of a new test to diagnose adult ADHD, but many clinicians believe an ADHD diagnosis can't be made based on one test. To make a diagnosis, your doctor will assess any symptoms you or your child has had over the previous six months.

Your doctor will likely gather information from teachers or family members and may use checklists and rating scales to review symptoms. They'll also do a physical exam to check for other health problems. Learn more about ADHD rating scales and what they can and cannot do.

If you suspect that you or your child has ADHD, talk to your doctor about getting an evaluation. For your child, you can also talk to their school counselor. Schools regularly assess children for problems that may be affecting their educational performance.

For the assessment, provide your doctor or counselor with notes and observations about you or your child's behavior. If they suspect ADHD, they may refer you or your child to an ADHD specialist. Depending on the diagnosis, they may also suggest making an appointment with a psychiatrist or neurologist.

ADHD treatment

Treatment for ADHD typically includes behavioral therapies, medication, or both. Types of therapy include psychotherapy, or talk therapy. With talk therapy, you or your child will discuss how ADHD affects your life and ways to help you manage it.

Another therapy type is behavioral therapy. This therapy can help you or your child with learning how to monitor and manage your behavior. Medication can also be very helpful when you're living with ADHD. ADHD medications are designed to affect brain chemicals in a way that enables you to better control your impulses and actions.

The ADHD Diet

The ADHD diet is designed to remove foods like sugar and food additives that are thought to exasperate the symptoms of ADHD, and replace them with good-for-you foods and supplements designed to boost concentration and improve brain functioning.

While many parents of children with ADHD already try to avoid or remove sugar from their child's diet, the ADHD diet goes much deeper. Here are the basic principals behind the ADHD diet:

- Avoid artificial food dyes, colors, and flavors
- Avoid artificial sweeteners
- Avoid foods and products that contain salicylates
- Avoid simple carbohydrates and sugars
- Avoid caffeine and alcohol
- Increase consumption of complex carbs
- Eat meals high in lean protein
- Increase foods high in omega-3 fatty acids

Many parents tend to use a more general approach to the ADHD diet. For example, they may avoid artificial additives and sweeteners and focus on creating meals that are high in protein and complex carbs, but may not go as far as eliminating salicylates.

Parents are also encouraged to try an elimination diet, where children are put on a very restrictive diet for a period of time before foods are slowly re-introduced one at a time. As each new food is reintroduced, parents look for reactions that may suggest an intolerance to the item. This can be tedious and time consuming as reactions can sometimes take weeks to occur, but if it helps identify which foods trigger or worsen your child's ADHD symptoms, it's time well spent.

Please note that the information above is not an exhaustive list of the Dos and Don'ts of the ADHD diet, and is intended merely as a starting point for those interested in pursuing natural remedies for ADHD. Always consult a licensed physician and/or naturopath before making dietary changes to ensure they are safe and suitable for you and your child, and to discuss important supplements your child should be consuming.

Much research suggests that children with ADHD can benefit from supplements such as omega-3, zinc, magnesium, and iron.

Kid-Approved ADHD Diet Recipes

While so many parents swear by the effectiveness of the ADHD diet in managing the symptoms of attention deficit hyperactivity disorder, it can be very overwhelming and difficult to make dietary changes in children, especially when they are head-strong, picky eaters. The good news is that there are HEAPS of kid-friendly ADHD diet recipes out there, and we've rounded up over 60 ideas to inspire you! Please note that these recipes follow the general ideas of the ADHD diet, but many of them contain allergens like wheat, dairy, soy, and salicylates. If you find your child reacts negatively to these foods, make sure to avoid them.

ADHD Diet Breakfast Ideas

One of the best things you can do for your child, regardless of whether he or she has ADHD or another developmental challenge, is to ensure he or she starts the day off with a protein-rich breakfast to fuel the day ahead. This can be difficult for those with food sensitivities, intolerances, and allergies, and while many of the ideas below aren't strictly ADHD diet approved in that they contain wheat, dairy, and salicylates, I still wanted to include them as I know many parents use a more high-level approach to the ADHD diet and need recipe ideas that are high in protein and complex carbs. For those who follow a more strict version of the ADHD diet, I suggest giving smoothies a try, and I've included a fabulous smoothie recipe book below to give you some ideas!

Cereal

You obviously want to steer clear of sugary cereals, and if your child doesn't tolerate dairy well, you can always use unsweetened almond milk or another nut milk of his or her choice. Multi-Grain Cheerios, Shredded Wheat, and Bran Flakes are all great cereals to consider, but these are certainly less desirable options for kids as they don't have a ton of flavor to them. Consider adding fruit like bananas and berries to provide a bit more oomph.

Oatmeal

Oats are a GREAT way to start the day. They're nutritious, high in soluble fiber, rich in antioxidants, and help keep blood sugars stable. Again, you want to choose plain oatmeal over flavored, sugary options, and can easily sweeten your child's oatmeal bowl with a banana, berries, dried fruit, and/or a spoonful of natural peanut butter. Cinnamon is another great natural way to add flavor!

Greek Yogurt Bowls

If your child can tolerate dairy, Greek yogurt is a great way to pack some protein into his or her morning. Add bran flakes, fruit, and natural nut butter, and you've got a delicious meal to fuel the day.

Breakfast Burritos

Cook up a batch of scrambled eggs with some preservative-free bacon and some of your child's favorite veggies, and wrap it all up with an organic whole wheat tortilla!

Natural peanut butter on whole wheat toast

Add sliced bananas for added flavor, potassium, and energy!

Smoothies

Kids love smoothies, and moms love that they offer a great way to get their children to eat nutritious superfoods like spinach and kale without them even realizing it. You can create so many different types of smoothies to suit your child's individual likes and dietary needs, and I love that you can prepare smoothie bags ahead of time to store in your freezer for quick, easy, and nutritious breakfasts on-the-go.

Eggs

A list of ADHD diet breakfast ideas wouldn't be complete without eggs. Whether your child prefers his or her eggs scrambled, poached, fried, or boiled, they are an excellent source of protein, vitamins D, B2, B6, and B12, iron, and zinc. Of course, eggs are a trigger for ADHD symptoms in some kids, so tread carefully, but if you can incorporate eggs into your child's diet, this easy breakfast casserole by Low Carb Yum is a great option to consider!

ADHD Diet Lunch Ideas

If your child follows the ADHD diet, it can be very difficult to find school-safe options to pack in his or her lunch. My best advice is to invest in a few bento boxes and some fun eating utensils so you can pack an array of different ideas your little one can snack on while at school. I'm a huge fan of YumBox as they offer many different lunch box sizes with multiple compartments, and they are completely leakproof, allowing you to pack both wet and dry foods in your child's lunch. I also love this set of Bento Box Lunch Accessories – it has tons of fun cutters and food picks to help you make an otherwise boring lunch fun and exciting for a child who can't eat all of the same things his or her friends can.

There are heaps of school-safe ADHD diet ideas you can pack inside a bento box. Make sure to include a good balance of protein and complex carbs to ensure your child's blood sugar remains constant throughout the day so he or she can concentrate. I've listed some ideas below, and caution you again that some of these include allergens like wheat, dairy, soy, and salicylates, so you'll need to pick and choose depending on how strictly you follow the ADHD diet and/or according to your child's food tolerances.

- Hard boiled eggs
- Cheese sticks and slices
- Greek yogurt (watch the sugar content in flavored yogurt)
- Preservative-free deli meat
- Rotisserie chicken
- Clean hummus
- Whole wheat crackers
- Veggie sticks
- Berries
- Fruit
- Dried fruit

You can also fill a thermos with your child's favorite smoothie or soup (check out this dairy-free creamy chicken soup recipe by How We Flourish), and if your little one tolerates wheat, there are tons of other options you can explore. Whole wheat sandwiches and wraps are an obvious option, and you might consider these 3-ingredient flourless muffins.

Oh! And if your child's school allows nuts (all of our schools are nut-free here in Toronto), see our ADHD diet snack ideas below for additional ideas to include in your child's packed lunches.

ADHD Diet Dinner Recipes

While some would argue it's harder to find packable ADHD diet recipes to put in a child's lunch, others would say dinnertime is more difficult as it can be quite challenging finding filling family-friendly recipes that are devoid of gluten, soy, dairy, sugar, and food additives. Thankfully, there are heaps of other parents out there who have already done the legwork for you, and I've rounded up 24 ideas to inspire you below! Again, these recipes support the overall principals behind the ADHD diet, but you will need to check the individual recipes to ensure they adhere to the degree to which you follow the diet and don't contain ingredients your child can't tolerate.

ADHD Diet Snack and Dessert Ideas

One of the toughest parts of having a child who either can't tolerate certain foods, or has a full-blown allergy to a particular food group (or 3) is that it limits their ability to enjoy the same sweets and snacks as their peers, which oftentimes leaves them feeling left out. If this sounds like your child, I suggest getting him or her involved in the kitchen to help him or her feel more in control. This can be a great way to spend quality time together, and you may surprise yourselves by creating delicious masterpieces together the whole family will love. Here are some great ADHD diet snacks and dessert ideas to get your started!

- Mixed nuts
- Trail mix
- Dried fruit
- Whole wheat crackers with nut butter
- Hummus with veggies sticks
- Apple or banana with nut butter
- Frozen bananas
- Fresh fruit kebabs
- Yogurt parfait
- Popcorn

While my recommendation is to opt for one-ingredient options wherever possible that don't include sugar or sugar alternatives, I wanted to include some basic dessert options to consider if you don't follow a strict ADHD diet and/or make exceptions for special occasions.

What Are Some ADHD-Friendly Healthy Snacks to Incorporate Into My child's Diet

Foods that are rich in fiber and protein may help kids with ADHD focus, concentrate, and learn. Keep these easy snacks on hand to sustain their energy and avoid triggering symptoms.

Healthy snacks that balance protein and carbs may help children with ADHD stave off hunger and reduce symptoms.

Like all kids, children with attention deficit hyperactivity disorder (ADHD) need to eat a healthy diet, and that includes choosing healthy snacks. But feeding kids who have ADHD can be extra challenging for several reasons. First, medications can decrease their appetite, says Angela Lemond, RDN, a Dallas-based spokeswoman for the Academy of Nutrition and Dietetics who specializes in pediatric nutrition and treating medical conditions through food therapy. Second, kids who experience hyperactivity expend more energy and may need more calories than some of their peers, she adds.

Snacks are key to staving off hunger and mood swings but not just any snack. While research doesn't support one definitive diet for ADHD, dietitians say some foods may help reduce symptoms. "Have a balance of protein and carbohydrates with each snack," suggests Lemond, since this combination provides an optimal nutrition package for sustained energy and concentration. Aim to keep blood sugar stable with plenty of fiber aim for 3 grams (g) or more per serving and limit added sugars to less than 5 g per serving, to avoid dips in energy.

These seven kid-friendly snacks are healthy and fun, too.

1. Mini Pizzas to Improve Concentration and Behavior

Mini pizzas are a fun, quick snack and you don't have to tell your kids they're healthy. Make a mini pizza on a whole-wheat English muffin (that's the fiber) with low-fat cheese (that's the protein). Protein may improve concentration and possibly make ADHD medications work longer, says Amy Kimberlain, RDN, a spokeswoman for the Academy of Nutrition and Dietetics and a wellness dietitian at Baptist Health South Florida in Miami. Fiber, a complex carbohydrate, makes food take longer to digest and keeps blood sugar levels stable longer, which is beneficial for kids with ADHD, because any quick dips in energy can trigger behaviors or impact concentration, says Lemond.

2. Fruit Smoothies to Boost Brain Function

Kids who have ADHD benefit from the vitamins, minerals, and fiber that fruit provides. Vitamin C and folate, in particular, play a direct role in helping brain function. Orange juice, oranges, and strawberries are all good sources of vitamin C, and they're all smoothie-friendly. For folate, try adding mango, spinach, and avocado. Bananas, another smoothie staple, are rich in vitamin B6 (pyridoxine), which aids in the formation of neurotransmitters that affect behavior.

Try making a fruit smoothie from fresh fruit and yogurt. Blend bananas, strawberries, orange juice, and ice in the blender (or any other fruits and veggies); add some yogurt for thickness; and serve. Choosing nonfat Greek yogurt will give your smoothie extra protein. "Balancing protein with fruit slows down the digestion process of the fruit, which helps release energy from the food more steadily." However, more protein is not necessarily better when it comes to kids, so there's no need to add protein powder on top of the yogurt. "A typical school-age child really only needs 7 to 15 g of protein per meal."

3. Hummus Spread on Pita to Help Kids Focus

Hummus is a Middle Eastern spread made from ground chickpeas and tahini (sesame seeds). It's a great source of plant protein and fiber, a Pittsburgh-based food, fitness, and nutrition consultant and the author of Fueling Young Athletes. Chickpeas and sesame seeds also contain iron and folate, which may help with ADHD by improving functions like blood flow and focus.

Serve the hummus on fiber-rich whole-wheat pita that you've cut into pie-shaped wedges. Try including colorful veggie spears for dippers as well.

4. Peanut Butter on Whole-Wheat Bread to Build Memory

For kids with ADHD and all other kids, too snacks should contain protein, which helps with memory and learning. One classic idea: peanut butter (an excellent source of protein) on whole-wheat bread (for fiber). Kimberlain also suggests half a tuna salad sandwich (some evidence suggests that children with ADHD may have low levels of essential fatty acids, which can be found in canned light tuna) or a whole-wheat tortilla with sunflower-seed butter and half a banana.

5. Veggie Sticks With Tasty Dips to Entice Kids With Dampened Hunger

When your child opens the refrigerator or kitchen cabinets, "you want them to see healthy snacks, not cookies, candies, or salty snacks." Cut up fresh vegetables for example, carrots, celery, and sweet bell peppers into bite-sized pieces and leave them in the fridge for easy snacking. "A healthful diet may reduce symptoms of ADHD by reducing exposure to artificial colors and additives and improving intake of micronutrients."

Peanut butter, cottage cheese, and low-fat dressings make great dips for cut-up veggies and may entice kids whose ADHD medications dampen their hunger, says Jessica Crandall, RDN, CEO of Vital RD. Lemond also recommends black bean or other bean-based dips.

6. Dried Fruits and Nuts to Boost Fiber and Protein

Dried fruits are another great source of fiber for your child. They have little protein, but they go well with nuts, which can provide the protein needed in a healthy diet for ADHD. A dozen almonds will net about 3 g protein. However, if you don't watch portion sizes, dried fruits and nuts can quickly add extra calories to your child's diet. That may not be a concern, since many kids with ADHD are hyperactive and need more calories anyway. But it's a good idea to divide the snack into small servings so your child doesn't overeat.

7. Snacks With Hidden Nutrients to Cut Down on Sugar

If your child with ADHD is a fussy eater, one way to get them to eat healthy snacks is to disguise the healthy ingredients. Try baking a healthier version of carrot cake or zucchini bread. "A diet high in sugar can cause swings in your child's blood sugar levels, exacerbating ADHD symptoms" but you can usually cut the amount of sugar in the recipe by a quarter or a third without affecting the taste too much. You may also be able to substitute applesauce for the oil.

Which Foods Are Good for ADHD and Which Can Make It Worse

In summary, snacks that contain a balance of protein and carbs are ideal for kids with ADHD. Watch added sugars and processed, low-fiber grains such as white rice, white bread, and white pasta. Avoid carbohydrate-only meals and snacks adding a protein like nuts, cheese, seeds, bean-based dips, yogurt, or milk allows the food to be delivered into the body in a steadier way that optimizes energy levels for conditions such as ADHD.

Stage 1: ADHD in Preschool

Could my high-energy child have ADHD

That's a common question parents have, because nearly all preschoolers are sometimes impulsive, fidgety, cranky or inattentive, chief psychiatrist and medical director at the Children's Health Council in Palo Alto, Calif., and a clinical professor at Stanford University.

Consult a pediatrician when behavioral problems actually impair a child's ability to learn, to socialize or to be safe, he advises. Signs include serious aggression, out-of-control impulsiveness for example, children grab objects that are off-limits, can't wait their turn or engage in physically risky behavior. If a preschooler has ADHD, "[our] primary focus is on helping parents improve their parenting skills."

One option he recommends: parent-child interaction therapy (PCIT), which teaches parents how to respond to their child's behavior. During an eight-to-12-week period, parents and children play while a therapist observes behind a one-way mirror and coaches parents through an earpiece on what to say or do. "It's good for the relationship, and both the parent and child feel better about themselves."

Ask your child's school or a child psychologist whether this, or similar behavioral therapy, is available in your area.

Parenting tips

- Offer positive feedback. When children obey rules, reward them with enthusiastic hugs or a few extra minutes with a favorite game.
- Don't reward bad behavior. When children act up in public, don't give in to their demands to avoid embarrassment. For example, if your child throws a tantrum in a grocery store, leave immediately. Shop later when someone can baby-sit or the child agrees to behave.

- Avoid excessive stimulation. Limit time with TV, computer and video games to no more than an hour daily to prevent sensory overload.
- Prevent social burnout. Limit play dates to one friend at a time and end the session while the children are getting along. This leaves them wanting more, with something to look forward to.
- Allow them to burn off energy. Schedule high-energy activity time daily in a controlled, safe environment. But avoid bedtime, because you want them relaxed and ready to fall asleep later.

Stage 2: ADHD in Early Elementary Grades

The peak time for an ADHD diagnosis is between ages 6 to 8 (grades 1 to 3). That's when symptomatic behaviors impulsiveness, hyperactivity and inability to pay attention start disappearing among the child's non-ADHD peers.

Your pediatrician may prescribe medication to control ADHD symptoms, but most experts, including Dr. Elliott, feel they do more harm than good at this age. The drugs are powerful and suppress appetite and growth, and "they're not helpful in kids this young very often."

Instead, behavioral therapies are preferred. Parents and teachers should set rules, offer rewards for good behavior and interact often with the child.

Parenting tips

- Be consistent. They'll learn to follow rules, which will make life easier for them.

- Praise them when they do follow the rules.

- Before bedtime, lay out your child's clothes and put everything they'll need the next day in a backpack so they don't have to make decisions in the morning.

- Use a "chore chart" so a child can cross out or put a sticker on tasks putting away clothes, doing homework, helping clear the table or brushing teeth as they're completed. Offer small prizes for completing at least 80% of chores in a day or week.

- Take at least 10 minutes every day to build good relationships for example, toss a ball, read a book, put a puzzle together, go for a walk or prepare dinner together. Don't criticize or reprimand during this time and focus on just having fun together.

- Continue to limit media time to an hour or less a day.

Stage 3: ADHD in Later Elementary Grades

Don't expect ADHD children ages 9 to 12 to control themselves as well as their peers do, Rooney says. They lag about two years behind their peers in their "executive functioning" the ability to control impulses or understand consequences of words or actions. That's why parents must be patient.

If your child's ADHD symptoms cause problems in school and at home, a pediatrician will probably prescribe medication such as methylphenidate, dextroamphetamine or atomoxetine, Rooney says. These drugs can be very effective in helping improve a child's impulse control and ability to pay attention. By fourth grade, kids have more homework, so continue to help them organize, complete and return it.

After school, allow them to decompress by playing and getting exercise. Then have a structured homework period in a set time and place.

Continue to limit TV and video games for kids ages 9 to 12, and delay giving them a cell phone as long as possible.

"ADHD children have a harder time transitioning off the screen because they get very engrossed, and it's hard for them to shut their attention off," Rooney explains.

Make it clear to your ADHD child that screen time is something to be earned, not an entitlement, she says.

"Interactive social activities and homework come first."

Parenting tips

- Check in weekly with your child's teachers to make sure homework is being turned in and that there are no behavioral issues. If your school has a website where teachers post notices and homework, check it nightly to make sure all assignments are completed.

- Provide backpack folders, including one marked "homework," to help the child keep papers organized. Ask the teacher to make sure assignments are left in the homework folder at the end of the day.
- Ask the teacher if you can borrow a second copy of any textbooks your child often needs for homework, just in case they don't bring that book home.
- Spend one-on-one time every day with your child just having fun.

Stage 4: ADHD in Middle School

Homework organization becomes even more important when ADHD children reach middle school. They now have more than one or two teachers, and it's important to develop a working relationship with all of them, Rooney advises.

Kids are probably spending more time with computer games and social media, including cell phones. So keep an eye on them, she says. Let them help decide how to spend their time and how they should be rewarded for good behavior.

"Instead of charts and stickers that you use with younger kids, change [rewards] to things more appropriate for tweens."

For example, if they complete homework with minimal fussing all week, they may earn a sleepover or an outing to a movie with friends. Kids are more likely to cooperate when there's a reward waiting and if they took part deciding what it would be.

Your pediatrician should carefully monitor any medication to see if adjustments are needed as your child goes through puberty.

Parenting tips

- Teach your child to use a daily planner; it's an essential organizational tool. Have your child fill out a schedule for each day.

- Create a contract with your child in which certain behaviors, such as completing homework and chores, earn more independence and rewards.

- Limit access to a cell phone. If your child has one, it should be turned off or put away during meals, homework and at bedtime.

Stage 5: ADHD in High School

Parenting an ADHD teen is even more challenging than with a non-ADHD teen, because they're likely to become more rebellious during these years, clinical director of ADD Centers of America in Chicago and a member of the scientific advisory board for ADDitude Magazine.

Don't take the rebellion personally.

"It's all part of growing up and developing their sense of self as an individual apart from their parents," he says. "If you chill out, they will too."

Parents must find a balance between the amount of structure teens need to be organized and one that they can tolerate, he says.

Although teens may have difficulty accepting parental rules, "they still have to have basic routines in place otherwise, they're lost."

Parenting tips

- Set and maintain realistic goals for yourself and your child. If more time is needed for tasks, pad the schedule.

- Have good supports in place for example, get tutoring help, find a counselor your child is comfortable talking with, set a regular sleep schedule and plan regular doctor visits to ensure the right medication and dosage.

- Listen to your teen, and focus on solutions instead of problems.

- Respect your child's privacy and personal space. Monitor their behavior at home, but do it from a comfortable distance.

- Increase privileges when your child demonstrates responsibility. These could include allowing an overnight stay at a friend's house, attending a local concert with friends (with a chaperone) or borrowing the car once the teen has a driver's license.

- Involve your child in discussions about rules and routines. This encourages ADHD teens to comply and accept responsibility.

- While there is no definitive ADHD diet, many sources claim that certain diets, foods, and meal plans can help reduce symptoms.

- Various foods can affect energy and concentration levels. Certain choices may, therefore, be better for people with attention deficit hyperactivity disorder (ADHD).

- Some research suggests that following specific diets such as elimination diets, the Few Foods diet, and the Mediterranean diet could play a role in managing ADHD.

Best foods for ADHD

Certain foods are better at keeping a person's energy and blood sugar levels stable and improving concentration. These foods may especially benefit people with ADHD. The following may be particularly helpful:

Protein-rich foods

- Eggs and whole-grain bread may benefit people with ADHD.
- Protein is essential for the health of the brain, and it plays a key role in producing brain chemicals called neurotransmitters.
- Including protein in a meal also prevents spikes in blood glucose levels. Some people suggest that these surges increase hyperactivity.

Foods rich in protein include:

- meat and poultry products

- fish and shellfish

- beans and lentils

- eggs

- nuts

Complex carbohydrates

- Like protein, complex carbohydrates can help prevent blood sugar spikes.

- Eating this type of carbohydrate also keeps a person feeling fuller for longer, which may stop them from snacking on sugar-filled foods.

In addition, when people eat them before bedtime, these foods may encourage better sleep.

The foods below contain complex carbohydrates:

- fruits

- vegetables

- whole-grain bread and pasta

- brown rice

- beans and lentils

Vitamins and minerals

Some studies link ADHD with low levels of certain micronutrients, including iron, magnesium, zinc, vitamin B-6, and vitamin D.

However, it is unclear whether these lower levels lead to the development of ADHD and whether consuming more of these nutrients can improve symptoms.

Nonetheless, they are all essential nutrients in the diet, so eating more foods that contain them is unlikely to cause harm.

People can find these nutrients in the following foods:

- iron: beef, liver, kidney beans, and tofu
- zinc: meat, shellfish, beans, and nuts
- magnesium: pumpkin seeds, almonds, spinach, and peanuts
- vitamin B-6: eggs, fish, peanuts, and potatoes

- vitamin D: fatty fish, beef liver, egg yolks, and fortified foods

Omega-3 fatty acids

Chia seeds are a good source of omega-3 fatty acids.

Omega-3 fatty acids are essential fats that a person must get from their diet. They play a role in heart and brain health.

Children with ADHD may have reduced levels of omega-3 fats. Some research suggests that consuming more omega-3s may help modestly improve symptoms.

According to an interview conducted by a group of nonprofit organizations called Understood.org, omega-3s may improve attention, focus, motivation, and working memory in children with ADHD.

However, they caution that more research is necessary and that omega-3 fatty acids are not a substitute for ADHD medications.

Some sources of omega-3 fatty acids include:

- fatty fish, such as salmon and tuna
- walnuts
- chia seeds
- flax seeds

Foods to limit or avoid

Adults and children with ADHD may feel better if they limit or avoid the following:

Sugar

Eating sugary foods can cause blood glucose spikes and crashes, which can affect energy levels. Some caregivers report a link between sugar consumption and hyperactivity in children with ADHD.

While some studies indicate a link between high consumption of sugar and soft drinks with a higher prevalence of ADHD diagnosis, other research finds no connection.

Even if it does not improve ADHD symptoms, limiting sugar intake is a healthful choice for everyone, as it may reduce the risk of diabetes, obesity, and tooth decay.

Other simple carbohydrates

Sugar is a simple or refined carbohydrate.

Other simple carbohydrates can also contribute to rapid changes in blood sugar levels and people should only consume them in moderation. The foods below contain simple carbohydrates:

- candy
- white bread
- white rice
- white pasta
- potatoes without skins
- chips
- sodas
- sports drinks
- potato fries

Caffeine

Small amounts of caffeine may benefit some people with ADHD some research suggests that it can increase concentration levels.

However, caffeine can intensify the effects of certain ADHD medications, including any adverse reactions that a person may experience.

Adults with ADHD should limit their caffeine intake, especially if they are taking ADHD medications. Children and teenagers should avoid tea, coffee, and cola completely.

Artificial additives

Some children with ADHD can benefit from removing artificial additives from their diets.

The American Academy of Pediatrics (AAP) recommend that children avoid these additives, particularly food colorings because they can worsen ADHD symptoms.

Artificial additives may also interfere with hormones, growth, and development.

Many prepackaged and processed products contain artificial coloring, flavors, and preservatives, including some:

- breakfast cereals
- candies
- cookies
- soft drinks
- fruit punches
- vitamins for children

Allergens

Some researchers claim that removing potential allergens such as gluten, wheat, and soy can improve focus and reduce hyperactivity.

However, eliminating these allergens likely only benefits those who actually have an allergy or intolerance.

Consider discussing food allergies with a doctor or dietician before removing these foods from the diet.

Diets for ADHD

While there is no cure for ADHD, many people discuss certain diets or foods that they believe can help manage ADHD symptoms, such as hyperactivity and difficulty concentrating. The following sections look at the research behind various diets that people believe may reduce symptoms of ADHD.

An elimination diet: Removing artificial additives

The AAP recommend that children avoid artificial additives, warning that they could worsen ADHD symptoms. Following a diet that eliminates additives would involve not eating:

- artificial colors
- artificial flavors
- preservatives
- artificial sweeteners

Many breakfast cereals, candies, and sodas contain these chemicals. Over the years, various researchers have looked into the effects of additives on ADHD.

According to a 2017 review, eliminating additives may have a small effect on ADHD symptoms. The authors suggest that the specific benefits may also extend to children without the condition.

The Few Foods diet

The Few Foods diet is a short-term intervention that helps people determine whether certain foods make their ADHD symptoms worse. It is highly restrictive and involves eating only a small number of foods that are unlikely to cause an adverse reaction.

If a person notices a reduction in their symptoms after eliminating certain foods, this suggests that a food allergy or intolerance could be making their ADHD symptoms worse. After beginning with the Few Foods diet, people gradually reintroduce other foods and watch for a reaction.

A different 2017 review confirms that the Few Foods diet could help children identify and eliminate problematic foods.

The Few Foods diet is extremely restrictive at the start. For example, one diet plan involves eating only lamb, chicken, potatoes, rice, bananas, apples, and cruciferous vegetables.

The Mediterranean diet

The Mediterranean diet is a safe diet for people with ADHD.

The Mediterranean diet is well known for benefiting the health of the heart and brain. It involves eating mainly:

- fruits
- vegetables
- whole grains
- legumes
- nuts

- healthful fats, such as olive oil

Some research suggests that not following a Mediterranean diet is associated with ADHD diagnosis. However, the results do not suggest that a Mediterranean diet could prevent or treat ADHD symptoms.

Nonetheless, because of the benefits to other areas of health, it is a safe diet for people with ADHD.

Other diet tips

The following diet tips may also benefit people with ADHD:

- Eat balanced meals. Try to include a mix of vegetables, whole grains, protein, and omega-3 fatty acids in most meals.
- Schedule regular meal and snack times, as routine is important for children with ADHD.

- Do not skip meals, as this could lead to blood sugar crashes and excessive junk food consumption.

- Keep plenty of healthful foods on hand for a quick snack, such as fruits, nuts, and chopped vegetables.

- Speak to a doctor about taking a multivitamin and multimineral supplement, which may be especially helpful for picky eaters and people with nutrient deficiencies.

- Check all ingredient labels on food packaging, and avoid foods that contain artificial additives and high amounts of sugar.

- Shop around the perimeter of the grocery store, which tends to contain the most minimally processed whole foods.

Sample meal plan for children

Try the following healthful meal plan for children with ADHD:

- breakfast: scrambled eggs with cherry tomatoes on whole-grain toast, and a small smoothie made with milk, spinach, banana, chia seeds, and frozen strawberries
- snack: sticks of cucumber and bell peppers with hummus
- lunch: a cheese and bean quesadilla with guacamole and salsa, and a slice of melon
- snack: trail mix with walnuts, almonds, and dried berries
- dinner: homemade salmon fish sticks, baked potato, and green vegetables
- dessert (optional): frozen chocolate pudding made with low-fat milk

Sample meal plan for adults

This healthful meal plan may be a good option for adults with ADHD:

- breakfast: avocado and eggs on whole-wheat toast, herbal tea or coffee
- snack: yogurt with berries and chia seeds
- lunch: a salad with baked salmon and quinoa on a bed of mixed leaves, cucumber, and bell peppers, topped with sunflower seeds
- snack: sliced apple dipped in peanut butter
- dinner: chicken and vegetable curry with brown rice
- dessert (optional): 1 ounce of good-quality dark chocolate, and herbal tea

Summary

Some research suggests that certain dietary choices may help with some of the symptoms of ADHD. However, the evidence is limited.

In general, the best diet for people with ADHD is the diet that doctors recommend for most other people one that is rich in fruits, vegetables, whole grains, healthful fats, and lean proteins. It should include limited amounts of saturated fats and junk foods.

People with food allergies or intolerances should avoid trigger foods. Also, some people require vitamin and mineral supplements, though it is important to speak with a doctor before taking them.

Made in United States
Orlando, FL
18 December 2024

56018154R00039